'What if writing drew a ci[...]
with a soft limit; whispere[...]
both at once—to clean the[...]
in a vernacular for us as w[...]
burning palms.'
— **Zarina Muhammad, The White Pube**

'A stirringly compassionate observation of the overlooked and passed-by lives in our world. Jamal Mehmood somehow captures the sentiment of Urdu poetry in the context of British capitalism's brutalising drudgery, with writing that feels simultaneously nostalgic and completely refreshing.'
— **Suhaiymah Manzoor-Khan, author of *Postcolonial Banter***

'A beautiful, intimate collection, exploring the fault lines of suffering and the necessity of stillness. Mehmood writes with soft grace and an unfaltering belief in divine benevolence, allowing us to clean the blood and imagine a better world.'
— **Hussein Kesvani, author of *Follow Me, Akhi***

'Willing to bear witness to the sacred in the everyday, Mehmood writes with unwavering humility of God, of grief, of grace. His words embrace what is most numinous about poetry, reminding us that it too exists beyond language—like the soul.'
— **Victoria Adukwei Bulley, author of *Girl B***

'*The Leaf of the Neem Tree* reveals remarkable depth as it peels back layers of language and histories. In the homes so brilliantly illustrated in these poems, there is refuge, comfort and joy.'
— **Gboyega Odubanjo, author of *While I Yet Live***

THE LEAF OF THE NEEM TREE

First published in the United Kingdom in 2021
by Hajar Press C.I.C.
www.hajarpress.com
@hajarpress

ISBN 978-1-914221-01-9 Paperback
ISBN 978-1-914221-07-1 EPUB eBook

A Cataloguing-in-Publication data record for this book
is available from the British Library.

Cover and interior art: Hanna Stephens
Cover design: Samara Jundi
Typesetting: Laura Jones / lauraflojo.com

Printed and bound in the United Kingdom by
Clays Ltd, Elcograf S.p.A.

THE LEAF OF THE NEEM TREE

JAMAL MEHMOOD

Contents

MIRPUR AND MARYLEBONE

THE SEA

In the name of God, most Compassionate, most Merciful.

And peace and blessings upon our master Muhammad, his family and his companions.

For my grandparents, Jaan Begum and Bashir Ahmed

AUTHOR'S NOTE

In Nandita Das's biopic on Saadat Hasan Manto, the talented Nawazuddin Siddiqui says the following phrase: 'Neem ke pathe kadwe sahih—khoon to saaf karte hain.' Roughly translated: 'Neem leaves may indeed be bitter, but they do clean the blood.' This simple metaphor has never left me.

When putting this book together and considering the threads that run through the poems and stories, I thought about language, history and bitter truths; about how to translate the spirit of older Urdu poetry into contemporary English. I leave the reader to judge whether these attempts have been anywhere near successful. As I progressed through the work, I realised that death kept appearing both inside and outside it, and that perhaps the bitter truths of death and its metaphysics were what tied the works together more than anything else.

Long before this pandemic that reminds us constantly of the loss of loved ones, the titular poem was written after the passing of an elder who meant so much to so many people. May God have mercy on him. After the funeral, I realised how used to the rites I'd become, how accustomed I was to the pile of earth that we communally poured onto the departed. This was coupled with an almost solemn contemplation of legacy and a sense of wonderment at those who are able to live in service of others.

I think now of the sages who don't fear death—who see it as a way to meet with their Beloved at last—and of what beautiful hearts they must have. I hope that this small offering of mine points in that direction, and that something worthwhile comes of reading it.

PLAYLIST

Nusrat Fateh Ali Khan – 'Allah Hoo Allah Hoo'
Matthew Halsall & The Gondwana Orchestra
– 'Kiyomizu-Dera'
Jay Electronica – 'A.P.I.D.T.A.'
Le Trio Joubran – 'Sur cette terre – Faraadees'
Nayyara Noor – 'Aaj Bazar Mein'
Narcy feat. Yasmine Hamdan – 'Space'
Prince – 'Money Don't Matter 2 Night'
Noor Jehan – 'Mujh Se Pehli Si Muhabbat'
Ka – 'I Love (Mimi, Moms, Kev)'
Gary Bartz – 'I've Known Rivers'
Brother Ali – 'Secrets & Escapes'
Earl Sweatshirt – 'Riot!'

FIX UP, BACHE!

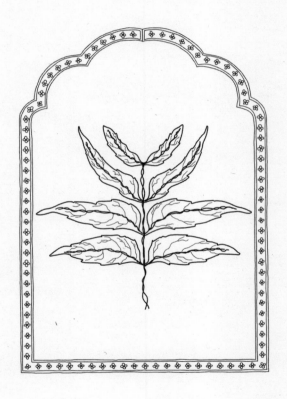

STORE-BOUGHT REMEDIES

The hair oil was stored behind the till like some vice. It was kept just below a large painting, depicting how the Ka'ba had changed throughout history and accompanied by an Urdu couplet that read, 'It is all from your generosity, Lord, that this affair is still going'. I was surprised by how much you could learn about a place by working in a grocery shop—who cooked with those packets of spice mixes, who had got married, who had gone to prison, who had been released, who had got indefinite leave to remain, who had joy and who was drained of it.

The herbal remedies were at the back—hibiscus, husk and stuff that I couldn't pronounce. I was reading the back of a packet of neem leaves one day when Salim Uncle, who'd started working at the store the week before, appeared behind me and said, 'It cleans the blood, bache—most sour things do.'

Salim Uncle was old. Old people didn't work in places like this; we all thought he should be at home watching Geo News, but he would laugh off our questions and tell us that he needed to keep busy, that the doctor said he needed more exercise. In any case, we never asked him to help with anything, out of respect. He was a good man but somehow had the perpetual, mysterious air of someone hiding something.

As soon as the adhan sounded from his phone, Salim Uncle would go to the prayer area at the back of the storeroom—a folded skullcap always ready in his shirt pocket, along with a pen I'd never seen him use. He cared about the details in everything he did. Since he'd started working there, I'd noticed that the prayer mats were perfumed, and the area was kept extra clean. There was a perfection in the way he prayed that I couldn't put my finger on; he really made it look like a sacred act and not just a combination of movements. The way one angular hand grabbed the other, as though he were locked into a higher spiritual state. His beard was a majestic horse-hair white, his clothes always immaculate. He wore his aqeeq ring on his right hand and carried a thin set of prayer beads, wrapped around his wrist. Some people lift you just by being there. Others, though, like Anwar, pull you right back down to the ground.

Anwar had finished university at the same time as me and found a grad scheme job, which paid enough for him to buy a new car that looked like it was designed by a fourteen-year-old boy. He now walked with his neck stuck out in front of him, got a haircut every week, and wore loafers and a watch that was too big for him. I could hear the derision in his tone whenever he asked me how things were, told me 'the firm' was still hiring, as if it were his dad's company. I didn't feel bitter—in fact, I was fairly sure he was on Microsoft Excel all day somewhere in the City, having to laugh at bad jokes and go for coffee with people who dressed like him. Abdullah Cash & Carry at least had some colour to it. He came over to me today to enquire about the job hunt again while waiting for his meat order. I was exhausted from the heat and told him I was actually starting to enjoy it here, but I'd let him know if I ever wanted to apply to 'the firm'. I had work to do, so I said my salams, leaving Anwar a bit confused. How could anyone, in this dunya, not want to be a consultant who wore turtlenecks?

Hashim was on the tills with Shabnam Aunty, wiping sweat from his forehead while packing a large cling-filmed slice of watermelon into a blue carrier. He wasn't very good at the chatting-with-the-customer part of the job at the best of times, and today he still looked visibly shaken from having seen a local uncle come out of the suspected brothel round the corner last night. He was a sweet kid; we'd miss him when he went off to university a few weeks later. I tried to keep it real with him about how uni wasn't a ticket to success, but I didn't want to dishearten him. Then again, my having worked here for months, unable to find another job after graduating, was probably enough of a reality check. It had been hard to say no—we knew the owner, and when he'd heard I wasn't getting anywhere, he asked me if I wanted to come and work at the cash and carry for a bit to keep me busy over the summer. I thought it would be a few weeks at most.

The shop was a bit too local at times. It's not ideal having aunties show you well-intentioned pity about the job market while you're trying to stack shelves with crates of chickpeas. After the first few weeks, that kind of thing had calmed down; it was mostly the same people coming back over and over, and there's only so many times they can wish you the best without it getting awkward.

I loved Shabnam Aunty like family. Like so many women her age, she loved through service, through suffering. She'd almost beg me and Hashim to take a break, to not drink Coke from the can, because she'd seen on WhatsApp that rats ran around the warehouses where they were kept, and she didn't want us to get ill. We called her the journalist—she knew everything about everyone, it seemed, right down to who was late on kameti payments. She was never evil about it though, or nosy—people just found her easy to talk to. She gave honest advice, sometimes unwarranted. Like when she told me to be realistic after seeing me talking to Halima. *Halima is a lawyer now,* she said. *Fix up first, bache.* I was annoyed for a while, but she was right. Halima was the opposite of Anwar in every way. Graduate jobs were purified by her acceptance of a training contract. The glittering star of outer London.

Shabnam Aunty had sensed how affected I w as b y her words that day. She slid me a small box of jalebis when we were both on tills and apologised in Urdu— for reasons I can't explain, this always makes forgiveness easier. 'Maaf kar do, bete, meri baat tumhe buri lagi na?' I could have cried. 'No, no, aunty, it's okay, koi baat nahi.' She asked me to forgive her anyway, and I had to comply. She was forgiven.

But fixing up played on my mind—what it meant, what I'd have to give or lose to get there. Shabnam Aunty treated anyone under thirty around here like her own child, and in some way, she was probably looking out for Halima. I played with the idea that Halima was the type of girl who wouldn't care about my job, all while arranging cake rusks by flavour on the shelves. Practically speaking, fixing up obviously meant a suit job, a salary, daily trips on the Central line, and maybe a haircut. I was okay with the salary and the haircut.

I tried using the money I made at the shop to help out at home, but Haris had a good job now and Abu still worked, so they always said I didn't have to. They didn't mean anything by it, yet I couldn't help but feel a little useless. Haris was a good older brother and a good son. He was always helpful to me, but I could tell he was frustrated too—we hadn't been friends for years. He had just walked into that older son role, helping out at home, driving people around, working his day job. He was my brother, but I had no idea what moved him or who he wanted to be. Outwardly, he appeared to be driven by a stoic sense of responsibility. There was a nobility in that, I thought, a quiet beauty in doing what you were supposed to do in spite of anything that pulled you away from it.

I always kept two photos in my wallet, enclosed in the notes section behind some old receipts. One was of Ammi and Abu on Haris's first birthday. I had taken it from one of the family albums. Ammi was wiping some cream off Abu's moustache, having failed at feeding him cake properly. Her smile was almost mischievous and Abu was palpably embarrassed, as family and friends watched this rare moment, at once intimate and childlike. The other photo was of Haris sitting on the chair in the old house, a peach-coloured sunscape covering half of his face. The worn-out dark green of the sofa under his light-blue jeans, snow-white socks, and that almost high-vis '99 World Cup Pakistan kit. I remembered him being annoyed when I'd asked him to sit so I could try out the new camera, but there was always a softness in him—for me, anyway—and he had sat and stared into the lens as if it were the rest of his life. It was still the best photo I'd ever taken. I had been chasing sunscapes ever since.

The Arab spices were kept next to the nuts, mostly untouched by customers, except a few Egyptian aunties who came in every now and then. I was trying to assist one of these aunties one day when Salim Uncle came up behind us, slapped my back and said something to her in what sounded like perfect Arabic. They both started to laugh. I ran up to him later and asked how he had learned Arabic. He smiled and said he'd tell me one day, but that for now I should be putting the flour sacks away.

We prayed maghrib together a few days later, and I enquired again after we finished. He turned to me on the mat and said he had spent five years in Egypt as a young man. He weaved through stories of Nasser, Al-Azhar and the pace of Cairo—it was like hearing a Naguib Mahfouz story in the flesh. He managed all of that without ever saying why, or how exactly, he had ended up there. Didn't sound like there was a grad scheme in sight. Talking to him made me feel like there was another path in life, but it always seemed to disappear when the world came into the room again.

I thought about Uncle during the walk home. His attention to detail, his impeccably trimmed white beard, his worker's hands, his simple prayer beads, his enunciation and his quiet incantations. I thought about going to Cairo. I wondered if Haris was ever going to be in love, whether Ammi and Abu were. I thought of Halima, and of how she talked to me like I was worthy.

SHRINES AND GUNS

He tells me that in Kashmir, a garden is only
worth its name if it bears fruit. A bagh
by any other name isn't the same. We all talk
about the friends of God, both real and
concocted—of sincerity of belief. Of salt-
water turned sweet and ointment for bad
hands. The swindlers of the uneducated and
sectarian myths. Of blasphemy and intuition.
Beheaded fingers while cutting grass and those
who shed tears at the sight of a familiar tree.
The face of a snake rubbed in chillies and
torched homes from communal violence.
Indian soldiers on the streets of Baghdad
and Indian soldiers in a London cemetery
and Indian soldiers in the British army and
Indian soldiers who became Pakistani soldiers.
I ask where my namesake fought and hope
the answer keeps away from Dhaka. A small
relief makes a home in my stomach. We
talk of rebellions and arrest warrants that

still existed until recently and I wonder if, in the quiet of night, these grandparents prayed for such boring grandchildren.

BURNING INCENSE
REMINDS ME OF WOMEN
READING THE QUR'AN

Of Arabic lodged in their mouths.
Someone has died, or a pink flower
has bloomed from the mud. In each case
a turn to God, for the departed or in gratitude.

Of sending repeated prayers on the one
with the black shawl, who held the arms
of the poor. Bangles talk quietly as date
pits are thrown to a pile like holy sport.

Of a ladies-only harmonising. The men
are elsewhere. The guests pray and line
their throats with hospitality they'll return
when their reasons rise above water.

Of wry smiles between the cousins who
hear their mother's sacred singing in public.
Who wait for the visitors to leave, to eat
leftover love and laugh at full volume.

KEEPING UP WITH THE CHAUDHURYS

We grow up on stories of apostles, caliphs and leaders
and pull on that energy to apply for graduate schemes.

A fascinating timeline of Jesus and the money changers
to multi-faith prayer rooms at Goldman Sachs.

There has to be more than a first-ditch attempt at banality
and more to show than turtlenecks and a mortgage.

I understand the sturdiness of old jewellery and
still remember letters in light-blue envelopes.

At a wedding we sit on a table with an old couple
and their silent child, who they tell me is going to LSE.

When they ask me what I do, I say I am a writer—
watch their faces light up as the mother remembers.

I like to think that she remembered being in love or
some other joy from before.

CRIMSON (FOR ZAYNAH)

Bronze and gold—both cousins of the sun;
these are things we have gone to war for.
Have let blood   water the earth,

maybe sacked a library or two before you
or I were born, into grass that still tastes
scarlet if you savour the ground enough.

If you look around and you find nothing
worth telling home about, stick to your
books   there's half a world in

those pages. If you find venom in the
mouth of someone who looks just like
you, take a moment to be with the breath

of God,   stay in
the sun and get as dark as you want. Your
Adamic skin is a cloak angels don't care for.

Nothing important like a book or a wish.
Keep your blood clean,   they say
some bitter leaves   can do that.

ASHK-E-BULBUL / اشک بلبل

(after Agha Shahid Ali)

When he asked for sugar, equivalent to 'ashk-e-bulbul',
she was proud that her daughter understood, in Urdu.

As in, teardrop of the bulbul bird in Persian—and
to indicate a very small amount, in Urdu.

Some refer to her as the nightingale of the East,
as if birds are as foolish as us: 'beh-vakuf' in Urdu.

Decades later, she tells that daughter's son the story,
that the man was from Lucknow, who spoke in
high Urdu.

When my grandfather died in Kashmir,
my mother said he had gone close to God, in Urdu.

Instead of saying someone passed, we say they have
become beloved to God, and I understand, in Urdu.

They call it a romantic language. I understand
why the boys listen to ballads in Hindi and Urdu.

When their hearts break, the mystery is in their silence,
a fist-wrapped secret I can just about hear in Urdu.

Jamal is an Arabic word, a name we borrowed with
its beauty,
which happens to be what it means, in both Arabic
and Urdu.

GRAVEYARD AS
GULISTAN-E-YAAD

Have you ever seen a man rush
to lift a coffin on his weary
shoulder? The trapezius was made
for this and for walking uphill
with a bag full of time, a resting place
for the head of a brother
known by all but blood.

What use is a friend who
wouldn't carry coffins
for you or with you? Use this
as your yardstick, because death
comes and makes fools out of
all of us—lays waste to what
we say to each other.

When he comes, all that's left
is what mattered, and three handfuls
of earth; the sheer confusion of loss.
A man leaves a hole it takes a village
to fill. Grief hits three generations
in one fell swoop, leaving the
bulbul to sing tears of joy.

TONGUE

Make dua for me, cry for me,
pour the Nile from your eyes—

beseech Him for me, friend
how do you make a prayer?

Translation is among our strangest
pastimes, both most and least fruitful.

Do you whisper or say it in your heart?
'Dua karna' is to do dua,

to do prayer, to make it—
to drop softness into coarse palms.

Eyes need cooling because the world burns,
take a short breath and place me in the middle—

sometimes I don't feel worthy,
can you lend me your longing?

What's life but a long ghazal anyway—
a lovers' meeting disallowed.

They call some deaths a wedding,
how brave and lovely!

Union is not for this life,
so make a prayer on my behalf.

Dua karna, beloved, in any tongue,
whichever comes most easily when you dream.

WHEN LOVE IS AT STAKE

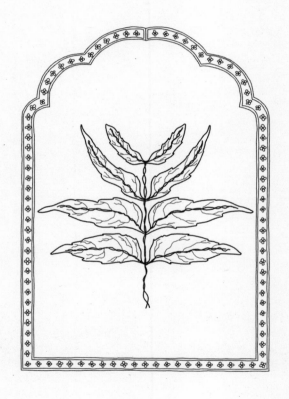

SHABAZZ, QALANDAR

The Sufis remind us to die before our death.
By the time that February arrived, Shabazz
had been living as a man who died decades ago.
He told the world as much, unflinching and glorious.

I haven't heard a man sound so resolute,
sound so much a man in all my years. To laugh
in the face of a threat, to pluck a tooth out
for all to see, how easy it was to dance with death.

The grace and lightness of foot required
to move through that world, shoulders strong
enough to keep the rifle steady when love is
at stake. A heart full enough to continue.

MIRROR

I smelt the wood of the floorboards. As sleep left my body, I noticed my legs, shoulder and hip were on the hard floor. I shuffled in the haze of what I assumed was morning light tearing through the window of my flat. Using my stronger left arm, I pushed against the floor to lift my chest off the ground. The TV was still on; some old documentary, I think, on Mohammad Rafi—they were playing that song where he asks the spring for a monsoon of flowers because his beloved has arrived. More sleep left me, and I was suddenly aware of the horrible pain around my left eye and nose. My whole body felt heavier, but my face in particular felt like it was carrying the rest of me. I struggled to my feet, the pain travelling through my age-worn body as I walked slowly towards the mirror in the middle of the room against a strange backdrop of love songs.

I stared, just breathing, at a version of myself that looked completely broken and yet somehow at peace. I wondered for a moment if I was dead, if this was Barzakh, but I didn't know how to check this, so left that thought as it was and carried on staring. My nose and left cheek were bleeding; I looked like I'd been beaten up but couldn't remember anyone being in the flat—in fact, I couldn't remember the last time anyone was here

37

at all. I thought maybe I had been robbed but found my phone, computer, TV and wallet were all there, as I looked around for evidence of a crime. All that was out of place was my hair—and my body.

Still half asleep, I searched the room slowly and painfully for reasons why I might have woken up on the living room floor. The food was still on the table, cold and splayed around a plate that was in pieces, amidst ruined letters and spilt water, the sun rays making a masterpiece out of it all. I started to remember fragments of the night before: microwaving the food, walking over the road to get the naan from Fareed's.

I returned to the spot where I had woken up. I concluded that I must have collapsed as I was putting the food down, though I had no way of confirming. The broken plate would explain the blood, and the position I had awoken in would match that turn of events too. I was unsure of what to do with the situation, so dragged my feet to the toilet to start the day. My face and body were still throbbing, yet numb at the same time. I brushed my teeth slowly and tried as best I could to slowly wipe away the blood with warm water, wincing each time I got too close to the fragility of where it hurt.

After living alone for so many years, I had grown used to not speaking to anyone, but it felt strange not having someone to sit with that morning. I turned off the TV and sank into the old leather sofa, staring into my phone. My nephew had come and fixed my phone a few months ago, taught me how to leave voice recordings to people. I opened WhatsApp to stare at my son's picture. He looked like he always did to me: a perfect combination of me and his mother. I thought about how far he was, how I didn't want to worry him—he had a family now, and an old man who'd collapsed halfway across the world was probably not what he needed. I'd never felt old until now. I needed to hear his voice. I wanted to hear what his life was like, but most of all I needed to tell someone that I didn't feel safe, as much as it would hurt my pride.

'Beta, this is Abu. Sorry if you're busy but I thought I could send you this recording. Abbas came and showed me how to do it. He's very clever now, he's going to secondary school soon but he's already very good with computers. Beta, I hurt—

'Beta, I wanted to tell you, I fell down last night. I'm okay, I just hurt myself. Behosh ho gya tha. I don't know how; I just woke up in the living room on the floor. Zyada fikr nahi karna, I just—I just wanted to tell you. You know I can't ask Azra baji, she has her own problems, but... beta, if you can ask one of your doctor friends to come and give me a proper check-up, you know? I think I should be okay, inshallah, I just got a bit worried. If you can't, it's okay, if you're busy, I'll go to the GP again, koi baat nahi.

'Chalo, beta, I hope you're okay, and the kids too, give them my salam, and Maryam as well. If you need anything done here, let me know. I can go to the bank or something for you, if you need anything. I can still walk!'

I felt a type of shame I was ashamed of. Why was it so hard for me to ask my only child for help? Why did he leave so soon after his mother died? Why did I expect him only to offer money, or some other useless thing? The truth, I knew, was more complicated than these simple questions. I only wanted the best for my son, and if that meant him following a job to the other side of the world, then that was what it meant. It didn't change my concrete loneliness though. That was something that lived in my stomach like a chronic disease.

I met Kevin at the old café. We called it the old café because there were always so many new ones popping up and closing down. He was shocked by my face, and his concern was endearing.

'Uncle, was it them racist guys that was marching the other day? I swear, tell me who it was, uncle, they can't be doing that to you! Let me call Mo!'

'No, no, son, it wasn't them. I fell over last night, don't worry about me. What's the problem today then? More essays?'

'Nah, I have to write a personal statement for if I wanna go uni. Can you check it?'

'Take this and get us some drinks first. And those pastries with the chocolate.'

I'd known Kevin since he was born, and his father far longer. Gideon always called me 'Professor' and asked if I could help him out when it came to Kevin's grades. It was my pleasure—it gave me a way to honour the friendship and keep myself busy, especially after Sundus died. Kevin was a smart boy but relied too much on his natural talent. He was a confident child, so I wasn't worried. I always told him it wasn't the end of the world if he didn't do well in an exam anyway, but that he shouldn't tell his father I said that.

Speaking to Kevin felt like my last connection to the young world. He remembered Sundus too, even though he was only a child when she left us. Sometimes he even gave me seeds to plant at her grave, which I visited every Thursday, pausing to pray before neatening everything up. Every time I planted something, I'd think of how Kevin was more connected to her burial place than my own son and the rest of my family were. I tried hard not to harbour any bitterness, but it seemed there was always something more pressing to them than old Uncle Hamid's problems. Conversations felt like an obligatory chore that people had to go through to keep me happy. I never complained about it. I couldn't bear to say anything that would make the calls dry up forever. Something was better than the coldness of nothing.

Kevin's personal statement was not due for a while. I started to go through his draft, circling words and asking why he had chosen them, what he might change and how he planned to close the essay. He was a little annoyed I didn't give more away as to what to write, but given how much time he had, I wanted him to get used to re-drafting and looking at his own progress. Watching him scratch with his highlighter in this old café in east London, I thought back to rote learning English poems as a child in Pakistan, not having a clue what I was saying, but enjoying how the words played in my mouth and sat in my mind, ready to show themselves to anyone I was trying to impress. There were of course problems with that style of learning, but the insistence on memorisation was something I was grateful for in later life. That was also something I had loved about Sundus: we had the same poems in our hearts. We were fortunate most of them existed in the form of songs. I always felt glad to have that piece of common ground between us.

Taking my last few bites of pastry and a sip of warm coffee, I stood up to leave, telling Kevin I'd see him soon. As I stepped out of the café and glanced across the road, my heart leapt to my throat. Right opposite, walking past the mithai shop: Sundus. In her unmistakable beige coat and soft, deep-brown scarf. My eyes followed her to see if I had made a mistake, but the woman continued to look just as she had a few seconds before. I made my way forward in her direction, trying to keep pace with her. In her left hand was a greasy paper bag. Spinach pakora. In her right hand, her usual white prayer beads. Black shoes, right heel slightly worn, henna on her fingertips. My Sundus.

She moved neither slowly nor fast, leaning slightly forward. She drifted past the shop where we had bought wedding clothes for Salim, past the butcher who knew my order before I spoke, past the place where I'd got the shoes I wore to Salim's graduation. I remembered how happy she had been that day. We had gone to west London to see our son graduate with his fancy west London friends. The sun was out and had painted Marylebone with even more money than usual. We had eaten at one of those Indian restaurants with a colonial-era aesthetic, the air outside smelling like earthy ground coriander, turmeric and other masalas, then and to this day. I sometimes went to Regent's Park for Friday prayers, especially in the summer, and would stroll past it each time. The trek across the city reminded me why so many people bent over backwards to live here.

My legs felt weaker than ever, but I was determined to keep up with Sundus. Where was she going? I didn't trust the vision enough to run towards her, fearing that she would disappear if I caught up with her. I was scared of shouting her name but couldn't help but mutter it under my breath. The feeling that I would collapse made me unsteady, but I had to keep walking. I stopped to take a sip of water from my bag, making sure I didn't lose Sundus in the crowd. She took a right, briefly sharing a glimmer of her face, and carried on. I continued behind her, not knowing where she was headed or where she would stop. But as I looked ahead, I started to notice the surroundings and realised where we were.

I knew the intricacies of this road like the back of my mother's hands, but in pursuit of Sundus I had completely lost my sense of geography. As she took a sharp left into the graveyard, I persevered against my body's sharp pains, trying to jog towards her. Beginning to limp, I found the courage to say her name out loud as she moved further away from me. I must have looked like a madman.

The smell of flowers filled the air as I entered. I could no longer see Sundus but instinctively walked to her grave, past the large trees and the sunflowers. There was no one there. I caught my breath when I arrived at where she lay, under all that earth—earth I had shovelled myself. By now my breathing was rough, like my oesophagus had been blocked by a cold metal pipe that my exhalations had to get past to be released into the world. I sat at Sundus's feet and wept like a child, ashamed of how I must have looked, my face stinging, my voice becoming hoarse through fumbled prayers, and the pain in my legs building until it felt like I had been spinning on a rotisserie for the last hour. I felt like death, lonely and undignified.

For the first time in ten years, I woke up next to Sundus. Upon realising where I was, I shook off the confusion like a wet dog and began the walk home.

BRICKS ARE ONLY
MOMENTARILY ORANGE

There was a time I didn't know
the word 'sunscape',
and it was just something I loved.

Like the sun when it held
a wall, and that first lick of van-bought ice cream
with the Flake.

Heat pressed the back of my
neck, darkening the skin; it warmed bones
and stirred honey into the bloodstream.

I rode a bike in public and was unashamed.
Knew only joy
and the temperature.

You were proud, and now so
much time has passed
that we disagree on where weight should be placed

when walking and
whether the skin should touch warm tarmac,
or be covered in leather.

OLD LOVE

(after Faiz Ahmed Faiz)

If you ask me for the old love,
know that it is different now
and there are other ways to die.
When you see a man buy and sell
the earth like it was a biscuit, it's
hard to not look over your shoulder
when you walk. So if you ask me for
the old love, know that it is different
now, and there are other ways to die.

Once you have seen shepherds in Arabia
compete with each other in building
skyscrapers, your faith is a little stronger
but you walk more slowly. If my lips are heavy
with tainted soil, I was searching for
water and hiding from air—so if you ask me
for the old love, know that it's different now.

Love, don't bother with that question—
you'd still embarrass the moon, but he's
staring out of the window with a sad playlist—
as it turns out the view is pretty clear from
there and there's no shortage of handguns.
One night in the middle of playing with
the sea, he mistook a predator drone for a
falcon and he hasn't been the same since—
it's different now there are so many ways to die.

GRAVELAND

I know of no cemetery this side of the cosmos whose
eyes shine at the thought of having me. Maybe once
a decade
they mention me in the valley, but it's been a long time
since anyone I've touched rested there longer than a wink.

Take me to the court of the sultan,
I'll audition to be the national poet of Qabristan.
Write our anthem on the ground in two and a half
languages in free-verse and adorn the earth.

In most graveyards I've been to, we've been assigned
the Muslim quarter, where I've been careful not to step on
barely marked graves, and read Arabic inscriptions
on the stones of others built to last.

I've met with flowers kept fresh by children and wondered
about the care in making sure even this place looks beautiful.
Like turbaned gravestones outside a mosque in Mostar
that give you
pause, when you notice almost all of them have the same
year of death.

ON FRIENDSHIP

On voice notes and memory
Gökyüzü and other kebabs

On we don't talk much anymore
but if I have a kid, you're still uncle

On aging and thunder
mosque stories that never die

On family and other extremities
the silence of comfort

On cut-grass Saturdays
give my salam to your mum

On the wave/s
honest opinions on trainers

On the pedagogy of the stressed
I'll keep them in my duas

On the apparition of decades
can't really tell anyone else

On the meaning of a smile
I'll come see you in Paris

On the forgetfulness of love
On the memory of spirit

BABU—NOUN (INDIAN):
A Respectful Title or Form of Address for a Man

Have you ever seen a man slowly unravel?
The betrayal of bones by the skin,
giving dap to Azrael before the night ends.

After five or six lifetimes, I imagine that
making peace with death is a plaything.
The words ring in my ears. I am nowhere.

He struggles to translate gabrahat into English,
his face home to a new blank space each day.
Sometimes we talk just to feel alive.

*

Until the talking walks slowly down
the stairs to start another day
altogether.

I mourn in private like Sunnis
for Hussain. Blood is important
to us—you are from our house.

'The Sunnah is three handfuls,
brother,' he says as we watch men
begin to cover you with earth.

My hands are so far from
the shovel and the dirt.
No touching the flowers

through this screen. Can't smell them
through the internet, but I know
the graveyard tastes like a neem leaf.

THE LEAF OF THE NEEM TREE

I bury more elders and shovel dirt onto their coffins.
The funeral prayer still escapes my memory.
I am reminded of its necessity each time I stand
shoulder to shoulder with those who stand for the dead.

Someone will vouch for them, volunteer to pay
their debts, be comforted by strangers and friends
and we will stand in the rain if we must,
palms to the sky like bewildered small men.

I have never once soaked the leaves of the neem tree
in water and proceeded to drink, but the moving years
are coming closer to the taste. I can imagine
the bitterness in my throat and can pray for clean blood.

I am told onions do similar work by my grandmother,
whose arms are still a house of God. I have lost hairs
as if they were opinions, found a question lingering
for each adage no longer true:

> Who was Mansur Hallaj?
> Is my blood spilt in Kashmir?
> What of Baghdad remains?
> Is Madlib the g.o.a.t.?

MIRPUR AND MARYLEBONE

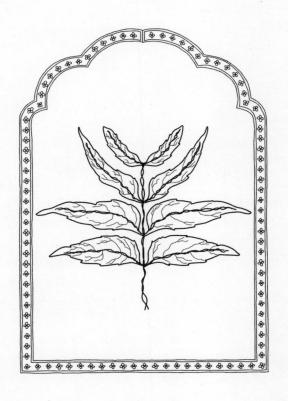

DO THE RIGHT THING

we came in too much peace if you ask me
but who am I to say what was necessary

to live

a man stops me in the street, asks me
if I'm local, what's the area like, how's the

racism

told him I thought the same thing but it's
okay alhamdulillah (bar a couple scribbles

on the bus stops)

I wonder what my child will look like and
how beautiful that would be no matter

what happens

there's a moment on earth with my name on it
somewhere along the line there's another

one for you

in between these two silences someone will
probably read mistranslated Rumi

there's a chance

I'll miss it if I'm too busy looking at you
and wondering how we got here

WALKING THROUGH MARYLEBONE BREEDS A LOVE OF MONEY

the higher the ceiling
the sweeter the fruit

      if you look too long
      at this place and its brothers

you will wake in the mornings
with a mouth full of copper and steel

      a lack of saliva and
      ears shorn of hair

free to hear
all the nothings you need

      behind your eyes you'll
      keep the names of horses

      and the floorplans of strangers' homes

(back home we say,
is it your dad's house?)

        baker street doesn't live under
        the feet of your aging mother

        even if you build a mosque there

the curvature of a lip
and the long mile of an eye

        do not need capital to burn
        but it's difficult to see

        with an eye full of ashes

'GET WORSE, O TROUBLE! ...'

goes the first line of the Munfarija. I am not as
brave as Imam Ibn Nahwi

but my therapist said not to respond with fear. She
uses the metaphor

of a clock that I can't take down, that will be in the
other room if I try

to go there. Tells me I have to drown it out—that
poetry is abstract

and I need to target the senses. I respond
apprehensively, listen to her

medicine. I think of cooking more, being outside
and touching the

soft life of plants. Even touching a pet, she says. It
all sounds so simple.

I'm no messenger but I think of the Arab Prophet
asking his wife

to cover him. I think of trembling, of being a
strange father.

Of my body temperature and neglecting
responsibility.

I think of the skin on my hands prematurely
turning to rubber.

I wonder what happens when you mix blood and
obsession,

if lineage pulls from that well, or if that's water only I
use over and over.

AGADIR

The tea was never quite as good here as at home, but it was somewhere to be that wasn't a shisha place or a restaurant. There was a strong scent of Lynx and musk from the neighbouring table, only slightly lessened when the three cups of cinnamon-infused tea arrived. Salma opened the lid and swirled the bark around a little, before opening the pack of biscuits that she had seen in the supermarket for 70p less than what she had paid here today. She was at the chai hut catching up with friends from school, exchanging stories on dissertations and failed rishta meetings.

Latifa kicked Salma's foot under the table and gestured with her eyebrows toward the well-perfumed group beside them.

'Isn't that Hafsa's husband?'

'Oh yeah, it is. So what?' responded Salma.

'Nothing, was just checking. Thought it was him innit.'

Hafsa was Salma's best friend, and her husband had just returned from a holiday in Morocco with his friends. Salma strained her eyebrows at Latifa for making her aware of this useless piece of information. She turned back to Jamila, who was discussing her thesis on the garment industry in Bangladesh, and how her Kashmiri parents were confused as to why she wasn't as interested in her own country.

'Just get Tasnima to do a master's about Kashmir and we'll be even,' said Salma, to peals of laughter from the group.

Latifa and Jamila rose to order some food and a tea to share, leaving Salma alone at the table. As she scrolled on her phone, something about the group next to her caught her eye. Like boys, two of the men were huddled closely, hiding something from the rest of their party. Sharif, Hafsa's husband, was showing his friend a series of suggestive pictures on his camera roll of a woman who clearly wasn't his wife. Salma almost dropped her phone, half-thankful that they weren't gawking at Hafsa, yet enraged by the crass display of disrespect towards the woman, and by her sense that her friend had been betrayed. Oblivious to the person behind them, Sharif carried on, tittering quietly and holding his fist out to his friend for a congratulatory bump after the slideshow. They continued to chatter within earshot, and each excuse that Salma contrived to exonerate him felt flimsier by the second.

'Was that the one who was in the lobby on the second night?' asked Sharif's giddy friend.

'Yeah, bro—she weren't even that expensive, said I could get a discount next time I come!'

Another fist bump, followed by childish snickers. Salma's face lost its colour. Latifa and Jamila returned to the table, and Sharif turned his head briefly as they sat down, only to turn swiftly back without looking in Salma's direction. Salma forced a smile at the girls, not wanting to make them suspicious, and used all her strength to stay and make conversation. She couldn't think about anything but Hafsa. Still living with her in-laws, quietly getting on with married life, while her husband was away on holiday paying for sex with other women. Was there just one? Was this a pattern? What did that even matter?

On her way home, Salma felt a panic unknown to her, her body temperature rising as she walked past familiar restaurants and clothing shops. She had never really cared much for Sharif, but Hafsa was happy, and that was all that mattered. She couldn't get Hafsa's sweet face out of her head as she deliberated over what to do—whether to tell her, and if so, when and how.

Arriving at her house, Salma went straight to her room. There were around forty minutes until sunset—enough time to shower before praying. Salma felt as if she needed to rub off the day's heat and the sight of Sharif laughing. She stood under the water for almost half an hour, recalling nights spent helping Hafsa to prepare for her wedding, her petal-like voice asking for friends' prayers, her father's tears as she left the house, her shining face on the wedding day.

After maghrib prayer, Salma sat with her face in her hands, imploring God for guidance as to what she should do. She asked herself what she would want in Hafsa's position and decided it had to be today. It would be better to do it here.

—Can you come over?
—Yeah, everything ok?

—Will explain when you come

—Salma are you ok?

—Yes, I'm ok pls come when you can

—Ok x see you in half an hour

Salma went downstairs to put the tea on for Hafsa. She needed something to distract her from the nausea. Every sound was louder than usual: the water splashing against the saucepan; her fingernails splitting open cardamom pods, like joints breaking; the loose tea sizzling to form a mixture like liquified ruby. She added the full-fat milk and watched it rise like a memory and simmer like anger. She went over the words in her head. *Your husband cheated on you while on holiday. Your husband is scum. Your husband was at the tea house laughing about it. Your husband was showing her off to his friend. He paid for it.* The tea almost spilt as it rose again.

Salma carried the teapot upstairs with some cups. Her room was warm, but she felt chills, along with a tennis ball of faint pain in the pit of her stomach.

The doorbell rang and she rushed to open it. She held in her tears as she hugged her friend.

'Salma, you're scaring me. What's wrong?'

'Just come upstairs, I'll explain.'

Salma's room was so familiar to Hafsa, its walls and its soft scent—a mixture of Salma's perfume and the faint savour of an essential oil, seeping into the air through the diffuser Hafsa had given to her friend for her birthday a few years ago.

'I don't know how to say this, Hafsa. I'm really sorry.'

'It's me, Salma, you can tell me,' said Hafsa assuredly.

Her eyebrows turned downward, her face preparing for empathy.

'I know, I know. Please sit down. It's not about me, though.' She took a breath. 'I went to the chai hut today,' she said cautiously. 'It was Sharif.'

At first Hafsa was more confused than concerned. 'What do you mean?' she asked. 'He was there? What happened?' Panic began to set in. 'Is he okay? I thought he was out with his friends. Is he okay?'

'Yes, yes, he's fine,' Salma soothed her. 'It's just... I think he cheated on you.' Her eyes closed, and the tennis ball of pain tightened.

'What are you talking about?' asked Hafsa in disbelief. 'Was he there with a girl?'

'No, with his friends. But he was talking about a girl in Morocco from their holiday last week. I'm so sorry, Hafsa.'

Hafsa wasn't looking at Salma anymore. Her teeth rested on her fist as she started to breathe more heavily. 'How do you know he wasn't joking around?' she asked quietly.

'Hafsa, I tried—I tried to come up with excuses for him, that it was all some long joke, but I could hear him talking about it, he was showing his friend!'

'Showing his friend what?'

'Showing him pictures—of her.'

Without realising it, Hafsa had broken. She pushed her face into the wall and sobbed, pleading why between gasps of air. The cold plaster gave way to the warmth of her friend's embrace, and she felt herself melting away.

Hafsa's nails dug into Salma's arm as she pictured Sharif with another woman, imagined him flaunting another woman's intimate pictures to a friend in public. The shamelessness of it, the sheer ugliness of it. She thought of their wedding night, then of someone else wrapped around him, of sleeping alone while he invited another woman to bed.

'Simmy, I didn't do anything wrong,' she gulped.

They fell into a long silence that neither of them knew what to do with. Hafsa's tears subsided and she drifted into a haze, watching her hands, thinking of home, of her life before marriage and the sudden disappearance of joy.

Salma rose to check the teapot was still hot before signalling to the window.

'Don't be silly,' Hafsa smiled weakly, realising what Salma had in mind.

'We're still thin enough to make it through! Come on, it's better to think outside.'

Just as they had used to, the two women squeezed through the window onto the roof, bringing an old blanket to sit on and reaching back through the window for the tea. They looked out at the houses in Sparkhill for a while. The summer breeze was slow enough to calm them.

'Simmy, what did she look like?' Each woman reviewed the image in her head of the girl in Sharif's photo, Salma's real, Hafsa's imagined.

'It doesn't matter what she was like. What matters is what he did, and that's wrong. You know Abid would kill him if he knew. If you want, I'll explain—'

'No, no—please, please don't tell anyone. It's only gonna cause trouble if... just let me think.'

They both fell quiet again, stretching their legs on the hard rooftop. Salma looked out towards the road, picturing the chaos of Hafsa's wedding, the music, the children running around, the smell of warm rotis in the tandoor that Aunty Shagufta had fitted in her garden that summer. Hafsa was remembering the same occasion, the hurt and the hope she had felt, the first touch of Sharif's hand that night, the colder that touch had become as time went on. She sipped Salma's sweet tea. It was always the same. One and a half sugars, two cardamom pods per cup, cooked well.

An hour passed like a short dream.

Hafsa broke the silence and spoke into the breeze. 'I think I'm gonna go home. I wanna go back home. I don't think I'll stay with him anymore. I don't want to look at him.'

Salma frowned. She understood, but she couldn't help but think of all of the confusion, suspicion and heartache that awaited both families.

Hafsa hugged her best friend and left for the short walk home. Her body felt heavy, as she swayed between resolute confidence in herself and feeling weaker than ever. Amy Winehouse sang 'Will You Still Love Me Tomorrow' into her ears as the lights of the takeaways, bakeries and restaurants blurred in her eyes. She had done this walk a thousand times. Summer evenings meant restaurants packed to the brim, the innocent laughter of friends, music escaping from peacocks masquerading as cars. All of this was so familiar, but today it felt strange and new. There were reminders of

Sharif everywhere; he had become an extension of the familiarity of home.

To have finished her degree, to have received a proposal from such a good family, to have had a happy wedding—everything had felt as it should have, until now. The walk home was like an unravelling. Hafsa looked for deceit in the eyes of strangers, trying to understand why he would do it, whether he'd done it before, how she would approach him. How would she avoid his kind parents when she arrived home, or humour them without breaking, when she felt like she had lost her footing in the world completely?

'Salam alaykum, Abu,' she said.

'Walaykum salam, beti, you okay?'

'Yes, Abu. Do you need anything?'

'No, no, beti, you carry on—Sharif is upstairs.'

Hafsa found Sharif in their bedroom with his headphones on, engulfed in some game. He raised both eyebrows in vague recognition of her entrance. She walked into the en-suite and hung her scarf on a hook behind the door, fighting back the desire to throw up in the toilet. Leaning over the sink, she looked into the mirror, a stranger to her own reflection. She washed her face over and over, like she had as a child, until the urge to cry left her.

She emerged to a still-oblivious husband and crawled under the covers, forgetting her ban against outside clothes in bed. Her insides traded fear for disgust. She flew back to the bathroom. Sharif turned quickly and threw his headphones to the floor to follow her, holding back her hair as she vomited, his soft hand on her shoulder as he asked what was wrong.

'What did you eat today?'

Hafsa was silent as she spat the last remnants of his filth into the toilet. Sharif flushed it away and stayed close as she rinsed out her mouth over the sink. She felt better, more prepared to face him.

'Hafsa, why aren't you saying anything?'

'Because I know about Agadir.'

Sharif's neck fell inwards into his stomach. Knowing and not knowing what she had found out, he followed her into the bedroom as she began to pack a small suitcase.

'What the hell are you talking about? Stop packing, Hafsa, you're being stupid!'

His palm fell on Hafsa's shoulder like a powder keg. She shivered away from his touch and turned to look him straight in the face, her eyes wide and strange. Sharif felt fear for the first time in their short marriage. He leaned back slightly on the bed.

'Don't touch me! I know what you did in Agadir. You're so disgusting, I can't even believe it. Tell me what I did wrong. Tell me why you'd do that, Sharif.' Hafsa's hands shook slightly as Sharif's silence slowly broke. He looked like a ghost.

'I don't know what you're talking about,' he said vacantly, turning away from her.

'Oh, for God's sake, Sharif, stop lying. I know what you did. I know about the girl from your phone.'

Sharif turned back, startled. 'Why are you going through my phone?'

'I haven't touched your phone! Someone saw you and heard you today. Just stop lying, Sharif. Tell me why, what did I do? Did I do something wrong?'

She felt like swearing the house down but thought about what his parents might think. Sharif's head was now in his hands, as if he had borrowed her silence from earlier that day. Hafsa shook him, trying to rouse him, to no avail. It took all the self-control she had not to hit him in the face until he bled. He looked so useless. Any love she had begun to feel for her husband in the past few months had completely withered and died. In the stillness that hovered between them, she imagined scattering its ashes around Sparkhill from Salma's roof. She retreated to her side of the bed and watched Sharif disappear in front of her.

'Who told you?' he said finally.

'What does it matter, Sharif? I'm done.'

'What do you mean you're done?'

'I wanna go home, Sharif. I don't want this. I didn't do anything wrong. I moved into your home, I'm good to your parents, I've cared for you, tried to help you with work, trusted you... I was perfect, and you still couldn't stop yourself. I'm gonna get my things and go home.'

'Hafsa, please, I'm so sorry. I don't know what else to say, it was just a mistake. Please don't go—what will Abu and Ammi say?'

'That's not my problem—it's yours. I swear to God, I won't tell anyone what you did, but what you tell them is up to you. I just want some time. I don't want to look at you.'

Hafsa had become stoic. Her demeanour and tone

were calm as she gathered clothes and essentials. Sharif continued to plead around her, panicking about his parents finding out, his breath rasping in his throat.

'So, what, you want a divorce now?'

'Maybe. All I know for sure is I don't want to be near you for now. If you care even slightly about me, let me go tonight. Sharif, you've done this yourself.'

Hafsa shook her head disappointedly with a slight smile. 'You didn't even wait long, did you? I trusted you were good, throughout this whole wedding and marriage. "What about Sharif, he's such a good catch, such a good family, knows what he's doing, head screwed on"—and I ate it all up. I don't wanna know what else you've done, who else you might be when I'm not there. There's something wrong with you, Sharif. What a name. Sharif!'

'I'll call you.'

'No, please just give me some time.'

Hafsa left as quietly as possible, propelled by a mixture of grief and her commitment to do the right thing. Staying in that stained house was something she couldn't handle, and neither did she want to be involved in Sharif's conversation with his parents. The safest place for her was with her family; they would ask her their own questions, of course, but these could at least be answered with less pretence and more understanding. What she wanted more than anything was absence—to embrace the nothingness of warm air and be alone. Away from a relationship she had walked into with so much trust, away from well-meaning loved ones, away from the impending stew of community whispers.

Left to stew in a pool of his own wrongs, Sharif was almost in disbelief—not only at his own shortcomings, but also at the way Hafsa had just turned and gone. He knew why she had sworn not to tell anyone; unlike him, she lived by her religious codes quietly and earnestly. She could have ruined his life. He could imagine her telling him why she hadn't. Her promise might save his parents from heartbreak; she did that for them, not for him. The sincerity of her voice rang in his head, and Sharif felt filthy. Filthier than that morning in Agadir, filthier than when he had told the air steward he didn't drink, filthier than when he had asked Hafsa to pick him up from the airport.

So lost was Sharif in his thoughts that he ignored the pain in his back from sitting up against the headboard. As he stared at the wall and pondered the person he had become, his alarm went off for the morning prayer.

WHITE APPLAUSE IN THE NORTH OF ENGLAND

Young boys in their crisp white jubbas (they will
call them thawbs, but do not speak Arabic)
march in a city centre in the North of England—
apologising, to piercing white applause.

They paint quite the picture in their small frames,
uniformly white topis hiding black hair,
oiled the night before by loving mothers, with no
sign of white applause;

their bodies covered by cloth stitched by their aunts
to the tune of a brutal white pittance,
cloaked in employment figures, avoidable
disasters—and white applause.

News cameras project the image into my home—
maybe pushing salt into my wounds
works like ointment for theirs, at home, as they sit
back, giving white applause.

If only I could tell you, bro, what it looked like to
see myself that way,
to have them think you were safe. For the good
ones, there is white applause.

KANAFANI'S REVENGE

I doubt it will be sudden that the cake seller
is not a student—anywhere. The day a piercing
clock on the wall will mean less than arid steps
toward Jordan or death.

You do not chance upon a hidden city.
Some places are only seen by the squinting eyes
of those in exile—to whom the cursive
of an eyelash is not lost to the blink.

I doubt it will be all at once that the cafés turn quiet.
Freedom is a moving spoon in a coffee cup,
the grinding of sugar and another morning
wet with last night's dew.

Beneath all our accords and deals,
stacked and tessellated like bodies thrown to rot,
there are those who imagine otherwise,
until that hazy dawn returns.

ON THIS EARTH / على هذه الأرض

(after Mahmoud Darwish)

a child eating fruit her ancestors had only heard of
in stories
a father teaching his child the wudu for the first time
a lover finding her beloved unwanting of anything else
dawn breaking on a prisoner who drinks the sun

Faiz's couplets
Malcolm's smile
the eternity of Arabic
salawat from Dakar to Delhi

the strength of coriander seeds crushed with stone
eating with your hands in the safety of company
a song shared by two generations
an old man's change of heart

a row of believers praying on the picket line
the silence of enemies in the face of interlocked fingers
a long-awaited victory and the memory of winter
a child waking up in Kashmir to find her father has returned

LAND OF THE PURE

He asked, well intentioned,
'How's Pakistan?'

'... Still there,'
replied the old man.

THE SEA

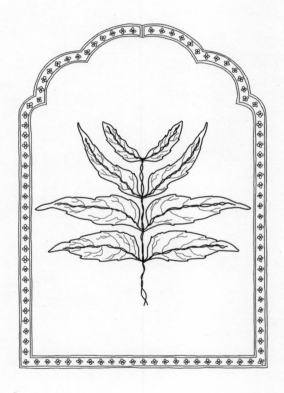

LITTLE ENGLAND '68

Stories had been circulating, as they always did, about the riches that England would bring. Chaudhury Jamil had built a house a few times the size of Rafiq's on the corner of the neighbourhood with money sent from England. It was physical proof that leaving was the only way out of the mess everyone was in.

Rafiq was one of the most inspired by these successes. He left Chitterpari for Karachi to find work, or to escape, or some mixture of the two. On his eighteen-hour train journey to Pakistan's second city, the house on the corner played like a film reel in his head. Somewhere for his family to sit peacefully, for his mother to rest her bones. The clean paint on the walls, a perfect contrast to the mustard road; the birds on the roof looking more majestic just by sitting on those new, high walls.

After one cycle of daylight, sundown and sunrise, Rafiq arrived in Karachi, and the city had laid out a banquet of sun for him. He was welcomed at the station by a relative, at whose house in Kemari he rested for a few days, before starting work at the port. The port was a new world, its scale unlike any workplace he'd seen in Kashmir or in the Punjab. Under the tutelage of another fairly new recruit,

Rafiq began the difficult work of cleaning the oil out of the bottom of ships. The pay was meagre, but enough to survive. He didn't yet earn enough to save anything, but he kept thinking of Jamil's house on the corner, and it kept him going.

Rafiq's days started early, and their highlight was the breeze at sunrise. The long walk in between containers, rope and steel was made beautiful by the relative silence and the morning's half-light, the friendly sea keeping him company when no one was around. With his time so engulfed by work, he began to cherish any and all hours outside of it, savouring each drop of tea, each morsel of food, the treasure of conversation and the peace of prayer.

A gruelling year passed, and the young, impatient man grew disillusioned with his few hours of freedom. The long days sat heavy in his bones, each one giving no answers or clues as to how he would build that house. Rafiq decided he had to try something else. He set out to convince his seniors to let him work on board the ships, and thanks to his work ethic and kind manner, they gave him a chance.

Over time, Rafiq built up a friendship with two of his co-workers, Muhammad Hussain and Haider Ali. He told them about the house on the corner, how England was the place you had to go to avoid a life of toil. He proved a deft salesman, and they soon bought into the dream of living on the little island. To plan their escape, the three men met after work, enveloped by artificial light and the aromas of sweet tea and street-cooked food that you couldn't find anywhere else.

'You guys look like you're planning a war!'

'It's war enough living here, don't you think?' replied Haider, smiling at the owner and placing a handful of small, crispy pakora remnants in his moustached mouth. They all studied the scribblings that Rafiq had made, lacing the excitement of boys with the pauses of men.

'We're going to England!'

'We only just got rid of them, and you're so eager to pay them a visit?' lamented the owner.

'Of course, some patriots have to go every now and then to make sure they don't come back. Don't worry, uncle, I don't want to stay there forever—they can't make tea like you! I'm not a Kashmiri like Rafiq, so the cold doesn't suit me anyway,' Muhammad chuckled.

They all laughed and continued to sip and nibble on the tray of fried goods. Haider, the quietest of the trio, was most inquisitive about the details of the plan—and more driven than even Rafiq.

'You're not scared, are you?' Muhammad asked Haider.

'Scared? Of what? You've seen the work we do here, you've been to my house, you've seen where I live, you've seen what awaits my children if they grow up here. A bank clerk, at most? God knows. However long the road is, I'll go. I'll see what they can do to me that hasn't already been done.'

'Alright, alright, hero. Let's get out of here before someone scouts you for a film or something.' Rafiq laughed and grabbed Haider by the back of the neck, as the men set off home for the night.

The next morning, Rafiq headed to the Public Call Office to make a phone call to his family. In his zeal to arrive in England, he hadn't even thought of going home to say his goodbyes. He knew his mother would be upset; he'd only been back once since leaving for Karachi.

'Aziz, pass the phone to Ammi, I haven't got long.'

'Yes, my son, how are you? Are you healthy? Are you warm?'

His mother's old voice crackled on the line, and he pictured her fragile bones gripping the telephone tightly.

'This is Karachi, Ammi, it's not that cold here. But listen—I've decided to go to England.'

'What? First Karachi and now England! Are you trying to get further and further from your mother? What about your wedding? I want to see your wedding—how am I going to see you if you marry some white girl in England?'

Rafiq smiled, his mind wandering to the house he wanted to build, covered in lights. 'I'll come back, inshallah,' he reassured his mother. 'I don't want to go forever! I can make some money there and send it home. Here is tough, Ammi. I make enough to eat and not much more. You all are at home and I can't help you. Don't worry, Ammi. Muhammad and Haider are coming with me. I'll send you a letter with all the information about when I'll arrive—please pass it to Chaudhury Jamil's son. I want to meet him there, someone from home.'

His mother wiped her tears in the call office. 'You're leaving me again, bache. You've decided, haven't you?'

'I've made arrangements, Ammi. We leave in a week or so. I'll come back, inshallah,' he repeated. 'I promise.'

'Call me from there. If you can't find work, you come back. We've been surviving this many years, we're used to it now.'

'Khuda hafiz, Ammi. I'll call you from there. Give my salam to everyone, I'll miss you all.'

What Rafiq had thought would be a formality had turned out to be a teary affair. He left the PCO wiping his eyes, trying to act normal in front of the teller, who'd seen this all before. He flagged down a rickshaw, confused at how emotional he'd become, wondering whether he'd decided on the right thing. He remembered the Jhelum River—the gashes on his legs from the rocks in the sea, from a time before he thought of money.

Rafiq had purposefully come to a PCO in the city; the long rickshaw ride home was one of his secret pleasures. Faisal Road, Jinnah's tomb, Frere Hall—and of course, his beloved noise. Laughter, bitter shouting matches, the horns of cars. It was a different noise to the clanging and bellowing of ships. A sound with more humanity in it. Rafiq was always attracted to this shimmer of the city and the aspiration in its noise. He savoured the warm wind in his hair for the last time, before stopping at a bakery for osmania biscuits dunked in hot tea. Customers huddled around the radio—Pakistan were playing England. Rafiq thought happily of how he would watch them live in London.

The men were all scheduled to work on a ship that would be docking in England—Rafiq's first big voyage. It was a Dutch carrier that would transfer the workers to another ship heading back to Karachi shortly after anchoring. The plan was painfully simple. The three men were going to escape before the return leg and would find a way on from there. They had the names of two towns and two acquaintances in England. None of them spoke much English, but they were young men, tired of their dirty work, tired of existing and tired of having nothing to show for themselves. The day came, and they stuck to the plan.

Not a soul at work had caught wind of the trio's intentions. They set off on a still spring morning. The seas were as calm as they had ever been, which the men took to be a good omen. They read the afternoon prayer on deck, entreating God to grant them a safe journey. As a Shia Muslim, Haider Ali usually attended a different mosque to the others, but he and Rafiq both prayed behind Muhammad Hussain at sea.

The voyage wore on longer than a month, through countries the men had never heard of, as well as those from the tall tales of colleagues—all on this route that had England at its end. The Suez, the white walls of Tunis and the rock of Gibraltar, which, bookish Haider explained, was a mutilation of 'Jebel Tariq', named after Tariq ibn Ziyad, the Muslim Berber who had taken the city centuries ago. Haider, lost in his thoughts that day, muttered some couplets from Iqbal, relaying to Rafiq and Muhammad that the poet was the last Muslim to pray in the mosque in Cordoba. As the ship slowed to a halt, pausing to meditate for a while, the three friends looked out at the rock from the deck, all contemplating the difference between themselves and Tariq, the conqueror.

They were due to dock in the early hours of the morning. They had heard England was cold but found a lukewarm morning and could see the shore in the distance. What they didn't know was that there were others with the same idea as them, on different boats, and that the British government had started to clamp down hard on those they suspected of bringing illegal immigrants to the island. On hearing of impending raids, the ship owners, knowing their Pakistani colleagues were unlicensed, informal workers, decided they didn't want the legal trouble of a smuggling charge or the risk of their operation being shut down altogether.

It was still dark when the three friends heard shouts from Dutch crew members, as lights from afar started to flash. The foreign cries became louder, and they realised something was wrong. Instinctively they ran away from the torch lights to the other end of the ship, where they hid behind tall boxes and tried to get their breath back. The captain and two others began to search the ship, pre-empting the English finding anything suspicious. Torchlight fell upon the limbs of the three cowering friends, tired and so close to their destination, as the Dutchmen raced to them with venom in their eyes.

The last thing Rafiq saw before being forced overboard was a blur of pale faces shouting in a language he couldn't understand, expunging three human beings from the ship like they were yesterday's litter. He screamed in protest, in Urdu, in broken English, with a fear so powerful that it shook even the men flinging him into the water.

Thousands of miles away from Kemari and their families, Muhammad and Haider struggled for their lives against the cold waves. They didn't know how to swim. Rafiq, raised by the banks of the Jhelum, tried with all his might to keep his friends' heads above water, but it was a losing battle from the start. They panted and thrashed wildly, crying out to the captain, who had turned away as soon as the deed was done. Rafiq tried to calm them, giving them desperate instructions as the brutality of the water sapped their frantic energy, both men maddened by the sudden change in their fate. They were so close. They could see the shore. Rafiq shouted for help through tears, as he watched his only friends in this continent slowly drown.

He swam back to the ship in defeat and pressed at the vessel's sides to catch his breath. Bobbing up and down with the waves, he recited the Fatiha and a short prayer, his gaze fixed through the strange funeral on the points in the sea that had last held his friends.

It would be excruciating, but he had no choice other than to try to swim to shore. Years of back-breaking labour had made him a strong man, and what he lacked in technique, he made up for in brute force. He removed most of his clothes and powered towards England. Each enraged stroke through the biting cold water brought a mountain of pain, but he knew that to keep going was his only chance of staying alive.

As soon as Rafiq felt land under his feet, he stopped to rest and find air, before slowly pushing through the heavy water. Barely clothed, he collapsed on the wet stones of England. Peering through half-open eyes, he discerned a white house, being circled by a majestic bird.

THEY'RE STILL COMING
AFTER ALL THIS TIME

There's a beach in Ostend I remember like a dream.
Paratha rolls for the journey and jaffa cakes in the
stranger's home. He produced an old logbook with
names, some of whom I think he helped cross the
Channel. A good man. Decades later he is dead, as are
two of those he helped set sail, if you could call it that.
Even later I tell my grandfather that more
people drowned off the Belgian coast, and he can't
believe that they're still coming after all this time.

The ocean floor murmurs with sin and history.
I go to a protest wearing clothes made in Bangladesh,
stand foot to foot and shoulder to shoulder with
the children of the Bandung conference on Fridays,
take a flight on a monster on Saturday. In the tunnel
there's an advert for a bank that is connecting us and
making our dreams come true and laundering money.
For your safety, please fasten your seatbelt and remain
seated until the seatbelt sign is turned off.

After all this time, the ocean still looks like sin.
Because of this I have now heard of Lampedusa
and Ceuta—joined to the shoulder blade of Morocco,
home to so many of those still coming after all
this time. 'To cross this sea,' he says in French, 'it
really makes you crazy.' A stone shaves the top
of the sea like a razor, staring back at whoever.
The sky is groomed by dusk in strange colours that
I can't name as easily as the continents under them.

OIL & WATER

Sooner or later it all comes crashing down,
they sang. Like a marriage or a manifesto—
look at our neatness, how it melts
like a plastic crown
or bubbling oil on the shore.

You can't live with crude oil in your throat.
Ask the seagulls their opinion of men
and tell me who is slick, tell me about
your favourite businessman
and his political views—I am all ears.

On Commercial Road above the ATM
some soul painted the words
'IS MONEY YOUR GOD'. Knowing
this place, it might have been removed
and put in the corner of an art gallery.

Around the corner he calls me
brother before he tries to sell me weed.
I want to stop and talk but don't know
where I'd start or finish. Maybe we both
read the Fatiha every day without fail.

MAMOUDOU GASSAMA

He was not a Western superhero because
he did not wear a disguise. Climbed four
balconies in the eighteenth arrondissement
with time to spare to watch the football or
to practise the word 'arrondissement' and
make it feel at home in his mouth. Masha
Allah, are the words you are looking for,
Emmanuel. If Mamoudou's child is born
next year, will the offspring of superheroes
be exempt from laïcité? Ou pas? How many
acts of heroism simmer underneath the cover
of the banlieue—or is that a veil you are happy
to let the people wear? We don't know how
this will end but there are stories already
written. A singing skull at the base of the Seine—
breath still fresh, soft tissue still warm to the
touch. Cold rain on the courtyard mosaic.

THE THIEF OF SUNRISE

l didn't know exactly when they had built the McDonald's there, but l knew those ugly towers were more recent. That stretch of beach was supposed to be one of the city's gems in an area most likely named after some angraiz. Clifton was where the British elite escaped from the city, and it remained a wealthy neighbourhood to this day. Home to consulates, a palace-now-museum and the houses of dynastic politicians, it had become part of the city from which it was once a refuge. Camel rides on the beach now competed with quad bikes, cheeseburgers and housing developments in the distance.

l walked up to the shore to let my feet touch the water. It was still a little dark, but there were a few others around, perhaps here to watch the sunrise or to get away from the chaos of the fifteen million people behind them. The sea looked the same, undisturbed by modernity, our gaze, or those who came here to wet their feet and forget some pain. The cool water filled the space between my toes and reminded me of a man l once saw making wudu before prayer at the Qaraouiyine Mosque. l had been struck then—not by his surroundings, the perfect crafts-manship, the tiles, the fountains, or even the tranquillity of the air, but by him. He had taken the water from the fountain and rubbed the cool, clear droplets over his arms and head with such purpose and calm that it was among the most beautiful things I'd ever seen.

I walked back from the water and took the janamaz from my bag, laying it out towards Makkah. My palms faced the sea in surrender, and I began to pray in a language I had learned too late. As I turned to my left to finish, I noticed a few more people had arrived, and some second-hand smoke tempted me before it drifted away. I moved to sit cross-legged and thanked God for the breeze.

Cities like this gave you a place to hide, everyone moving too fast to notice you've spent hours at the tea house with an unopened book and your seventh small cup. I had relocated here after years of wondering what it would be like to live in a city, having always been near one, or on the outskirts, never knowing what it actually felt like to be held by an urban sprawl. I thought of friends who talked about London or Birmingham like it was a friend in their inner circle, a theory only they understood, something I could never grasp, no matter how much time I spent there. They spoke of how the city felt, how their neighbourhoods were worth the name and neither sterile nor quiet. How people lent each other their hands so easily and softly. How the sun seemed to set just for them. I had come here to steal the sun—to see if after all these years I could restart a life, if it would rise for me like it had risen for them. Amma's love had been all the sun I needed before she became beloved to God. With her gone, I needed somewhere to go and rest these bones away from skies that weren't mine.

I had chosen to move to her city, a place I'd visited as a child, where I'd kissed the earth, smelt the sea and fallen ill to the food. Somewhere estranged but homely. England and London had become ever more unbearable, as more and more shards of glass were added, as the people I loved had left. I had decided on a city of lights and carnage, one where my solar-powered self could at least heal. My doctor had advised that the warm climate would do my bones good but that I had to watch my diet. I found it hard to manage the latter part of his request; perhaps the heat on my bones would offset the consequences of oily food. I thought of Ahmad, who'd returned to Sierra Leone a few years ago, and the summer afternoon we had spent on the canal in Hackney, while he told me about his poems and how he hibernated in winters, explaining why I never saw him.

Karachi was difficult in its own way, but I was prepared to humble myself before its chaos. One evening early on, I made my way to the market to look at old books. The spectacled man at the storefront had called out to me.

'You've come again!'

'What do you mean?'

'You wanted English books at the Urdu bazaar, remember? I sent that boy to fetch those translations for you.'

I laughed. He was right—I had come here years ago with my mother to search for translations for my research, and he had served us tea while his assistant left to find some books for me. He had been kind to

Amma, asking the chaiwala to bring her biscuits. She had made sincere small talk about her hometown and asked him if he knew who lived upstairs. She was always inquisitive about old buildings. Some of these ones had been built before Partition, the man had said, and Amma had flown away on a beautiful tangent about restoring one. An ever-curious reader of history, she always wanted to visit the world's Old Towns, making a patchwork story with photos and unverified tales from unofficial guides. She had worn a sombre white kameez that day, with blue beads and delicate embroidery around the neckline and wrists, the left of which bore her gold Casio watch that never went with anything but was a gift from my father. Her hands were always regal.

I was shocked the shopkeeper still remembered me and made my way over to give him a hug, hoping he'd call for some tea. As I sat with him, quietly anxious that he might bring her up, I felt as if the city was opening up to me for the first time, that my wound was covered here. I no longer felt like I had plastic lips. My life was buoyed by simple conversation with this stranger, my muscles loosened on the plastic chair, my jaw unclenched into that brief opening, my hands still. I left his company enthused in a new way, the evening heat no longer uncomfortable but sitting with me peacefully.

That night, I took a taxi to Clifton beach and finally cried. I shed tears over my distance from those I had left, for those who had left me. I cried into the sand and prayed for Amma, thinking of burials and the image of my mother in white. How they wore white at funerals in Indian films. How she whispered to herself and lit up the night.

In the morning I went to Seaview to be with the unchanging sea. A body so proud, upright and strong, that still found a path to beauty despite our encroachments at its edges and our sins in its belly. As the sun began to appear on the horizon, the amateur photographers shifted position and began to set up shop, as if this didn't happen every day. The warmth grew imperceptibly under my skin, and I felt close to everyone who wasn't there.

So much here was unknown, and it was rare to be given attention. But there were small victories. I knew my neighbour's children and taught them English on the roof. We watched the birds together and they asked me about my family. I asked them never to stop speaking Urdu. I kissed the hand of the old man who sat at the door of the mosque. On some nights I spoke to old friends. When I missed anything or anyone, I would go to the sea and think of them, undisturbed. The city had begun to fit in my hand, but not without making me sweat. It was a small price to pay to keep my bones warm.

TAKES A VILLAGE

The only place I know like the back of my hand
is the back of my hand, and sometimes
he could be jivin' too. In my head they know me
in Mirpur and Gillingham. On some nights they
mention my name in Karachi and perhaps once
a decade it's uttered in Rajouri,
but I doubt many can put a face to it there.
They still ask about me at the mosque at home
—my only claim to community. No other place
smells like elders before they died.
I can visit home for a few hours every week,
to feel like a guest, or a friend of my father.
How long are you allowed to claim a place before
you are accused of lying? Before they stop listening
and the food you left out is no longer edible,
like spoilt fruit of a whole town's labour.

AFTERNOON AT THE TOMB
OF ABDUL QADIR AL-FASI

I was on the border of shame but didn't have the right papers. Asked him how to teach a child two languages. He said, you speak Urdu to them and she should speak Arabic. We can't see past the flesh but some people by their skin alone remind you of God. They shared food with us that tasted like balance. A saint is buried on every corner in that city. The day after we took the divine name together, I woke for the morning prayer without an alarm for two days straight. Sufficient proof that holiness loves company. What is sin but a withdrawal symptom anyway. 'Yes, we bear witness'* as ancestral cry of all sinners. Of every language and hymn sheet.

* The Qur'an, 7:172.

LIMINAL

Take me some place where wet black kohl
is painted around my eyes. Let it run down my face,
let me run at pace. Let me get somewhere
when I am out of breath. Give me the satisfaction
of a terminating joy and all the grandeur of small victories.

There is something false in the big ones, like a claim
at divinity. The men who claim to be gods are just
lowercase g's. A celestial laughing stock, the dust
on a stolen slipper in the mosque courtyard.
Give me freedom from this child's play.

The abandon you feel for a second playing in a warm sea.
The weight of the blue expanse, your back to the world,
the world's back to yours. Water holding your skin
with the care of a new lover, under the eye of a jealous sun.
If all daybreaks were so kind, perhaps this wouldn't be earth.

SHEHR-E-JAANAAN / شہر جاناں

There is no dumbing of ecstasy where we wish to go.
No mockery
of the flesh—we are not called names in the city of
my Beloved.

There will be no metaphors for pleasure.
This place has no time or space for indications.

I am dreaming, like Mahmoud, about things I've
never seen,
but can only think of beholding after death.

Most of it is unknown, like the feeling of returning,
or sitting
free with your mother, eating home-grown olives in a
morning salad.

We of suffixes and lineage and capital—the rain is more
obedient than us.
The sweat of the clouds and soft perfume of the earth,
sweeter than my breath.

What does it feel like to have your name in the mouth
of an angel,
to be known in the heavens—to be held by light?

TO WHOM ALL
BEAUTY POINTS

Each curved eyelash is a sign

Before there was us there was You

The yearning of Indians for the dust of Medina

Before there was us there was You

A strained shoulder to touch the black stone

Before there was us there was You

A frail thumb kisses beads three hundred times

Before there was us there was You!

ACKNOWLEDGEMENTS

All praise is due to God—any goodness in this work is through His blessing. For any mistakes and short-comings, the blame is my own.

I want to give thanks to my parents for all their love. For their help and insight with Urdu translation and for all their prayers. To my siblings, Ayyaz and Aroob, my grandparents and the rest of my family, you have my love and my ear.

To my wife, Saffana, for her companionship, care and unending desire to see me succeed. I love you more than I can say.

To my friends for their support of my writing, love and memes. In particular, Sean Mahoney, Zia Ahmed, Ayodapo Aiyeola, Suhaiymah Manzoor-Khan, Victoria Adukwei Bulley, Qasim Ashraf, Ankush Jain, Rahima Begum, Mabrur Ahmed, Tasnima Uddin, Undleeb Iqbal, Sumairah Miah, Sulagna Roy, Adil Yaqub, Nabeel, Aqeel and Haseeb Mirza.

To my teachers, Mimi Khalvati and Roger Robinson—you taught me so much in such a short time. To Maulana Saaleh Baseer for the inspiration and knowledge you share.

To Hajar Press, for their patience and warmth, for trusting me with this work.

If I were to dedicate this book to anyone other than my grandparents, it would be to the memory of my elders—some of whom are no longer with us, and who seem to be leaving us more and more often. In particular, Khizar Hayat Khan Lodhi and Anwar Khan, God have mercy on them, both of whom I am indebted to, as are so many others from Gillingham and beyond.

To anyone I have forgotten, forgive me.